Who am I?

Name: _____

Personal Objectives: _____

_____

_____

_____

_____

_____

_____

_____

The Steps to Personal Effectiveness

Take action
and put your
learning into
practice

Step 4

Learn how to
adapt your
behaviour to
interact more
effectively with
others

Step 3

Learn how to
recognise and
appreciate
others'
differences

Step 2

Step 1

Explore and
discover more
about yourself

YOU
are unique.

You will see the world differently from the way other people see it.

Perception

Two people can look at the same thing and yet both see something different.

Your unique view is formed by your own individual perceptions and beliefs. If you can understand where these perceptions and beliefs come from, you can then begin to understand why other people see things differently. By understanding people, you can begin to appreciate who they are and improve your relationships with them.

The Ladder of Perception

When we perceive events and occurrences, the data received through our senses goes through an internal 'filtering' process. It is this internal filtering that makes us respond to things in the way we do. In his work on personality and organisations, Chris Argyris (b.1923) introduced the concept of an internal ladder to describe this process. The rungs of the ladder depict the psychological steps we go through between perceiving an event and responding to it.

Exploring the rungs of your ladder, in relation to a particular event, can help to bring much of what is unconscious into conscious awareness.

Because we don't all see things the same way, we don't all respond in the same way.

8

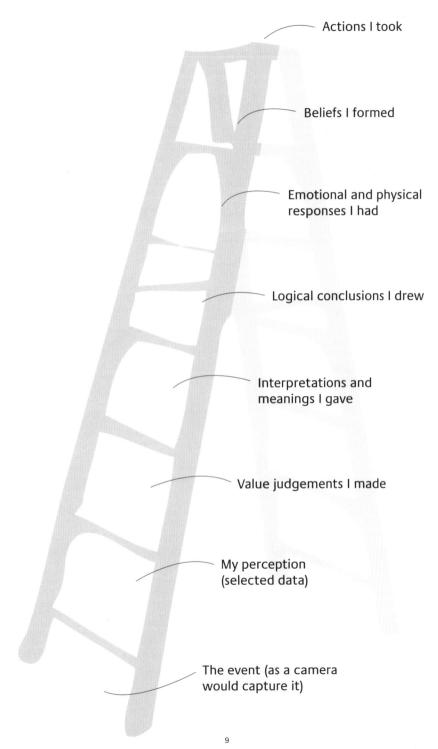

Actions I took

Beliefs I formed

Emotional and physical responses I had

Logical conclusions I drew

Interpretations and meanings I gave

Value judgements I made

My perception (selected data)

The event (as a camera would capture it)

9

Look at the list of
characteristics below. Circle
the ones you feel describe you.

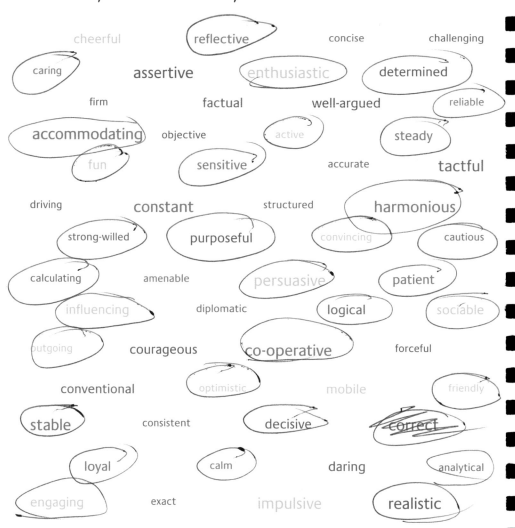

cheerful   reflective   concise   challenging

caring   assertive   enthusiastic   determined

firm   factual   well-argued   reliable

accommodating   objective   active   steady

fun   sensitive   accurate   tactful

driving   constant   structured   harmonious

strong-willed   purposeful   convincing   cautious

calculating   amenable   persuasive   patient

influencing   diplomatic   logical   sociable

outgoing   courageous   co-operative   forceful

conventional   optimistic   mobile   friendly

stable   consistent   decisive   correct

loyal   calm   daring   analytical

engaging   exact   impulsive   realistic

Add the number of words you have circled in each colour:

Blue	Green	Yellow	Red
4	11	11	4

The Discovery Colour Energies

The origins of personality trait theory date back to ancient Greece and Hippocrates. Hippocrates observed four distinct groups of characteristics, which he labelled the 'Four Humours'. He determined that once he could identify what type of 'humour' a person had, he could predict their likely behaviour.

Many researchers have subsequently expanded on this knowledge, and Insights has built on the extensive work of Swiss psychologist Dr Carl G Jung (1875-1961) to develop the Insights Discovery learning system.

This system uses four distinct colour energies which you can apply in your daily life to help you understand why you behave in the way you do, and why other people might behave differently.

What other words can you think of that describe your key characteristics?

Your Colour Mix

The colour I use most is: _____
_____
_____

The colour I use least is: _____

Write your key characteristics from the previous page in each quadrant.

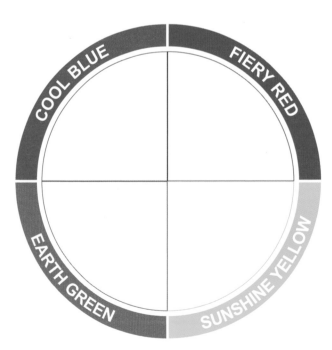

We each have all
four colour energies
within us; it is the
combination of the
four energies that
creates the unique
YOU.

Individuals with a preference for Fiery Red energy...

Are active and move in a positive and firm direction

Have a strong determination that influences those they interact with

Are single-minded and determined in their focus on results

Approach others in a direct and straightforward manner

Seek an outcome that is specific and tangible

16

When have you used a Fiery Red approach?

Individuals with a preference for Sunshine Yellow energy…

Radiate enthusiasm and encourage participation

Enjoy and seek the company of others

Approach others in a persuasive, engaging and inviting manner

Have a desire to be involved

Like to be noticed and appreciated for their contributions

18

When have you used a Sunshine Yellow approach?

Individuals with a preference for Earth Green energy...

View the world through what they value and what is important to them

Seek harmony and depth in relationships

Defend what they value with quiet determination and persistence

Prefer democratic approaches that respect the individual

Ensure all individual perspectives are heard and considered in making choices or decisions

When have you used an Earth Green approach?

Individuals with a preference for Cool Blue energy...

Desire to know and understand the world around them

Maintain a detached and objective standpoint

Value independence and intellect

Think things through before committing to action

Like information to be accurate and complete before proceeding

When have you used a Cool Blue approach?

Colour Summary

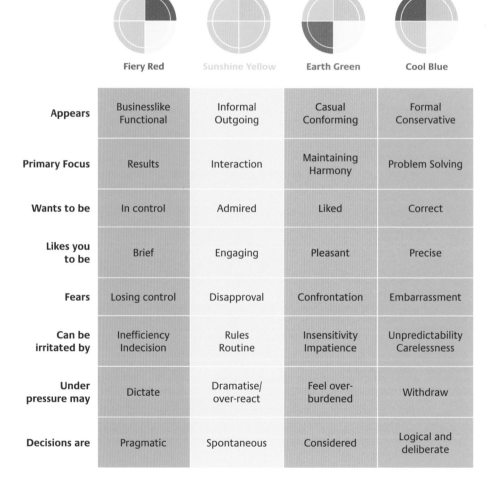

	Fiery Red	Sunshine Yellow	Earth Green	Cool Blue
Appears	Businesslike Functional	Informal Outgoing	Casual Conforming	Formal Conservative
Primary Focus	Results	Interaction	Maintaining Harmony	Problem Solving
Wants to be	In control	Admired	Liked	Correct
Likes you to be	Brief	Engaging	Pleasant	Precise
Fears	Losing control	Disapproval	Confrontation	Embarrassment
Can be irritated by	Inefficiency Indecision	Rules Routine	Insensitivity Impatience	Unpredictability Carelessness
Under pressure may	Dictate	Dramatise/ over-react	Feel over-burdened	Withdraw
Decisions are	Pragmatic	Spontaneous	Considered	Logical and deliberate

The Jungian Preferences

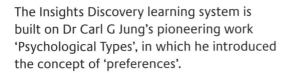

The Insights Discovery learning system is built on Dr Carl G Jung's pioneering work 'Psychological Types', in which he introduced the concept of 'preferences'.

Your understanding of these 'preferences' is fundamental to the way you communicate and build relationships with others.

Your 'Attitude'

Jung differentiated types according to their general attitude. He defined attitude as people's way of reacting to outer and inner experiences. There are two attitudes: he named and distinguished these attitudes as Introversion and Extraversion.

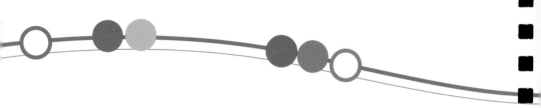

Mark the position on each scale which best describes you.

Introversion		Extraversion
Quiet	←——————————→	Talkative
Observant	←——————————→	Involved
Inwardly focused	←——————————→	Outwardly focused
Depth focused	←——————————→	Breadth focused
Intimate	←——————————→	Gregarious
Reserved	←——————————→	Flamboyant
Reflective	←——————————→	Action oriented
Thoughtful	←——————————→	Outspoken
Cautious	←——————————→	Bold

Your Decision Making 'Functions'

Jung classified people into either 'head' persons, who prefer to make decisions by thinking things through rationally using the 'Thinking' function, or 'heart' persons, who prefer to evaluate and make decisions subjectively using the 'Feeling' function.

Mark the position on each scale which best describes you.

Thinking   Feeling

Formal	←——————+——————→	Informal
Impersonal	←——————+——————→	Personal
Analytical	←——————+——————→	Instinctive
Detached	←——————+——————→	Involved
Objective	←——————+——————→	Subjective
Strong-minded	←——————+——————→	Flexible
Competitive	←——————+——————→	Accommodating
Particular	←——————+——————→	Ambivalent
Task focused	←——————+——————→	Relationship focused

The Discovery colour energies are a combination of the 'attitudes' (Introversion and Extraversion) and the 'functions' (Thinking and Feeling).

Jungian Preferences and the Colour Energies

Cool Blue energy is the combination of **Introversion** and **Thinking**. This combination produces a style that is task-focused, calm under pressure, thoughtful and objective. There is a powerful ability to investigate, observe and think things through. In making decisions, logical conclusions are carefully deduced after examining the evidence.

Fiery Red energy is the combination of **Extraversion** and **Thinking**. This combination leads to applying logic, reason and objectivity to structure and organise the external world. There is an outward focus and an ability to respond quickly to external events. Impersonal processes and logical guiding principles are used to determine actions.

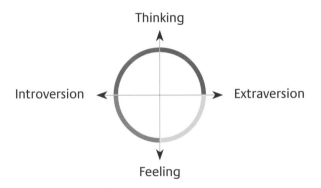

Earth Green energy is the combination of **Introversion** and **Feeling**. This combination results in an approach that favours reflection, harmony and consensus. With an inward focus, value-based judgements are made after reflecting on subjective experience and deeply felt personal beliefs. Personal motivation is largely determined by values and principles.

Sunshine Yellow energy is the combination of **Extraversion** and **Feeling**. This combination of preferences couples sociability and consideration for others with being action oriented and entertaining. There is a focus on involvement and interaction with others. Response to external events is based on one's values, beliefs and the desire for positive relationships.

Your Perceiving 'Functions'

Jung said that we view the world using a combination of 'Sensation', to record the sensory details, and 'Intuition' to see patterns, make connections and interpret meaning. He called these the perceiving functions.

He described these functions as 'instinctive, above and beyond reason, flowing from the unconscious and lying deeper within us'.

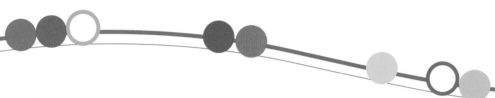

Mark the position on each scale which best describes you.

Sensation		Intuition
Specific	←———————+———————→	Global
Present-oriented	←———————+———————→	Future-oriented
Realistic	←———————+———————→	Imaginative
Consistent	←———————+———————→	Unpredictable
Down-to-earth	←———————+———————→	Blue-sky
Practical	←———————+———————→	Conceptual
Precise	←———————+———————→	General
Factual	←———————+———————→	Abstract
Step-by-step	←———————+———————→	Spontaneous

The Colour Energies with Sensation and Intuition

When we access Fiery Red energy combined with Intuition we can set a 'big hairy audacious goal'[1], with no requirement for a plan on how to get there.

Combining Fiery Red energy with Sensation helps us to establish the step-by-step action plan with milestones that will get us there.

[1] Jim Collins – Built to Last: Successful Habits of Visionary Companies

How and when do you combine your colour energies with Sensation and Intuition?

The Jungian Preferences work together rather than in isolation.

Sensation	Colour	Intuition
	●	
	●	
	●	
	●	

The Eight Types

There are eight distinct personality types in the Discovery learning system.

Once you have established the colour energy you use the most and the one you use the least, you can determine which of the eight types you might be.

1. Tick the larger circle in the quadrant of your most used colour energy.

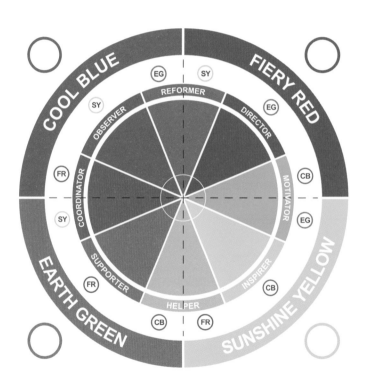

2. Staying in that quadrant, put an 'X' in the small circle that represents your least used colour energy.

X marks the spot of your Discovery type. Now take a look at the table on the opposite page

	On a good day	On a bad day	Likes	Goals	Fears
Director	Decisive Self-reliant Courageous	Impatient Forceful Aggressive	Competition Being in control	Success Progress	Losing control Failure
Motivator	Assertive Dynamic Enthusiastic	Indiscreet Hasty Manipulative	Adventure Unlimited opportunities	Prestige Respect	Being restrained Lack of recognition
Inspirer	Sociable Optimistic Expressive	Unreliable Unpredictable Too talkative	Interaction Getting involved	Popularity Approval	Disapproval Loneliness
Helper	Engaging Encouraging Empathetic	Emotional Gullible Needy	Intimacy Affection	Making a difference Connection	Isolation Rejection
Supporter	Caring Amenable Patient	Compliant Passive Stubborn	Being of service Accommodating others' needs	Harmony Acceptance	Change Conflict
Coordinator	Thoughtful Diplomatic Dependable	Anxious Withdrawn Hesitant	Order Security	Correctness Duty	Disorder Risk
Observer	Consistent Precise Organised	Reserved Defensive Detached	Logic The facts	Understanding Objective truth	Confusion Time pressure
Reformer	Self-disciplined Dedicated Pragmatic	Blunt Insensitive Critical	Rigorous thinking Problem solving	Excellence Perfection	Criticism Lack of respect

Recognising Types

There are specific techniques you can use to identify the mix of colour energies that people use.

We will examine 'clues' to the four colour energies, so that you become an expert at noticing them and responding to them.

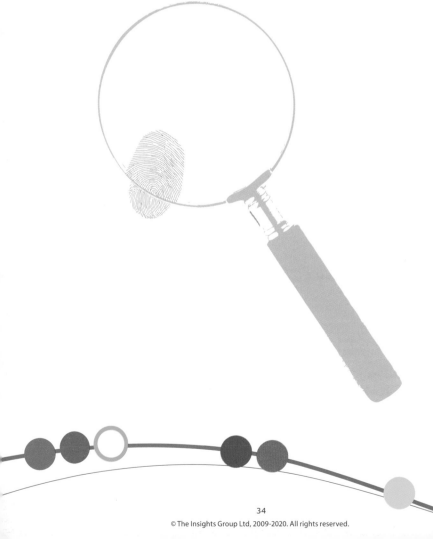

Every time you meet someone you have the opportunity to practise your skill of recognising and adapting to their colour energies.

Verbal Style

Mark on the scales where you think your and your colleagues' verbal styles are.

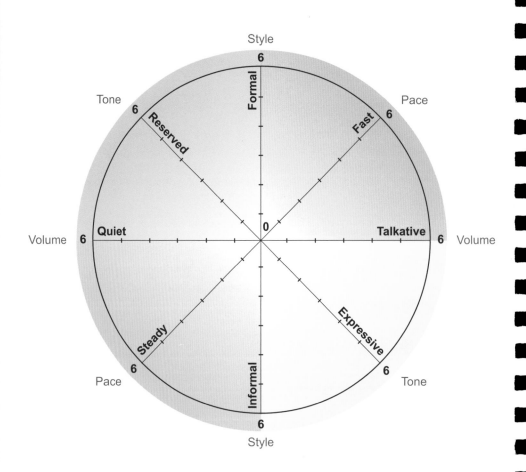

Body Language

What colour energy clues do you observe?

Recognising Types

Think of three people you know well.

What clues may indicate their use of the four colour energies?

Which colour energies do you see and not see?

Loud and fast pace of speech.

Informal manner.

See Sunshine Yellow and Fiery Red.

Don't see Earth Green or Cool Blue.

Mr A. Example

1.

3.

2.

The Insights Discovery Personal Profile

The Insights Discovery Personal Profile is a detailed personal report that describes your typical characteristics and behaviour.

Your Profile was generated as a result of you completing the Insights Discovery Preference Evaluator.

The Insights Discovery Personal Profile
Overview

As you read through this section, underline those statements that you think are highly accurate. Put a question mark next to those you don't agree with.

Overall, how accurately does this section describe you?

What stands out for you most?

The Insights Discovery Personal Profile
Strengths and Weaknesses

Use these pages from your Profile to gain a deeper understanding of the upsides and downsides of your psychological preferences.

What are the three key strengths and
three possible weaknesses that you think
are most accurate?

Key Strengths

1.

2.

3.

Possible Weaknesses

1.

2.

3.

How have these
strengths and
weaknesses shown
up in your life?

The Insights Discovery Personal Profile
Effective Communication

These pages are aimed at helping others to understand how to communicate effectively with you.

Select one or two statements that are most important when communicating with you.

Now read the Do Not statements. Select one or two that are most important.

Review your 'Value to the Team' statements and select the one or two that best describe your strengths.

The Insights Discovery Personal Profile
Colour Dynamics

Persona (Conscious)

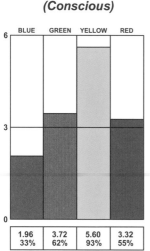

| 1.96 33% | 3.72 62% | 5.60 93% | 3.32 55% |

This is a direct representation of the scores from your evaluator. This is the style you choose to present to the world.

Preference Flow

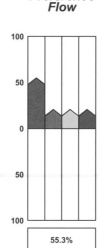

| 55.3% |

This shows where you were channelling your energies at the time you completed the evaluator.

Persona (Less Conscious)

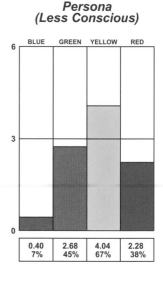

| 0.40 7% | 2.68 45% | 4.04 67% | 2.28 38% |

This is derived from Jung's theory of polar opposites and represents how you might react instinctively.

What do you notice about your own graphs?

The Insights Discovery Personal Profile
Insights Discovery 72-Type Wheel®

The Insights Discovery Wheel provides a visual representation of the four colour energies. You will notice from your Insights Discovery Profile that you have one or two positions on the Wheel. These link directly to the patterns (order and number above the line) of the four colour energies on your Conscious Persona and Less Conscious Persona Colour Dynamics.

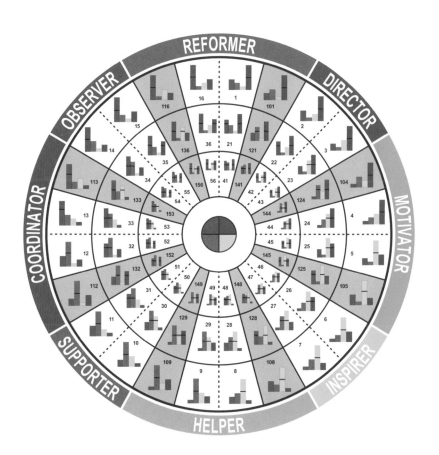

This wheel gives 72 combinations
of the Colour Energies.

Plot your own position on the wheel and the positions of some people you interact with.

What do you notice?

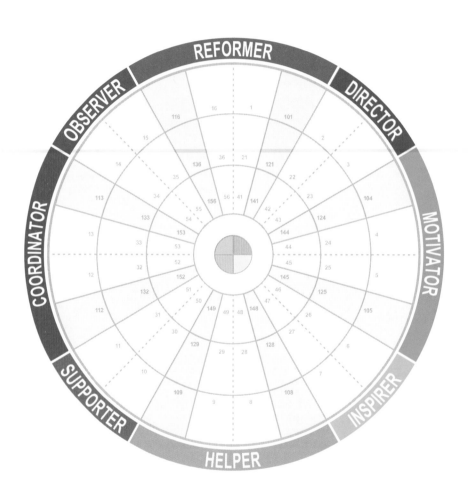

What could you do differently to enhance interactions with these people?

The Insights Discovery Personal Profile
Suggestions for Development

This section makes some recommendations as to what you could do to make the most of your strengths and develop your weaknesses. Look also at the Personal Achievement chapter, which focuses on several highly important aspects of your personal development.

Document the statements that you think you would benefit most from.

Why?

What difference will it make?

Committing to Action

What have you learned from this session?

Based on what you have learned, what will you focus on next in your journey of self-discovery?

Define one goal and complete a G-WAVE action planning sheet.

G-WAVE Action Planning

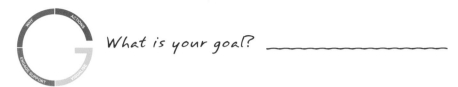

What is your goal? _____

Why is this
important
for you?

What actions
will you take to
achieve the goal?

Whose support
will you need?

What will it look
like when you have
achieved the goal?

What is your goal?

Why?

Actions

NEXT STEP

Visualise

Engage Support

51

Reflection on The Steps to Personal Effectiveness

Your journey continues…

What is my key action?

How will I adapt my behaviour?

What do I appreciate about the styles of others?

What did I discover about myself?

"Every advance, every conceptual achievement of mankind has been connected with an advance in self awareness."

– Dr Carl G Jung